Specimen Sight-Singing Tests

Grades 1–5

Notes

1 In the exam, the sight-singing test will be accompanied by the examiner.

2 The test may be sung on any vowel or to sol-fa, at the candidate's choice.

3 In each grade, separate bass-clef versions are provided for a selection of the tests. For practice purposes, teachers/candidates may make bass-clef transpositions of treble-clef tests in order to cover the full range of parameters. In the exam, male candidates should inform the examiner whether they are treble- or bass-clef readers.

4 Candidates will be given a short interval of up to half a minute in which to look through and, if they wish, try out any part of the test (unaccompanied) before they are required to perform it for assessment. The examiner will play the key-chord and starting note before the preparation time.

5 After the preparation time, the examiner will again play the key-chord and starting note, after which the candidate starts the performance, setting his or her own pulse and shadowed by the examiner at the piano.

GRADE 1

1

vocal range

key-chord and starting note

Lively

2

Dancing

3

Moderato

4

Sadly

5

Andante

6

Allegretto

7 (𝄞) **Moderato**

7 (𝄢) **Moderato**

8 (𝄞) **Andante**

AB 3445

GRADE 1

8 (𝄢) **Andante**

9 (𝄞) **Andante**

9 (𝄢) **Andante**

GRADE 2

1

vocal range

key-chord and starting note

Con moto

2

Espressivo

3

Allegretto

GRADE 2

4

Moderato

5

Espressivo

6

Andantino

7 (𝄞)   **Con moto**

7 (𝄢)   **Con moto**

8 (𝄞)   **Andantino**

8 (𝄢)

Andantino

9 (𝄞)

Dolce

9 (𝄢)

Dolce

GRADE 3

1

Poco allegro

2

Scherzando

5 **Expressively**

6 **Calmly**

GRADE 3

7 (𝄞)   **Cantabile**

7 (𝄢)   **Cantabile**

GRADE 4

3 Gently

4 Espressivo

7 (𝄞) **Cantabile**

7 (𝄢) **Cantabile**

8 (𝄞)

5 **Delicately**

6 **Larghetto**

7 (𝄞) Grazioso

8 (𝄞) Lento ed espressivo

8 (𝄢) Lento ed espressivo

AB 3445

Printed in England by Halstan & Co. Ltd, Amersham, Bucks.
02/12